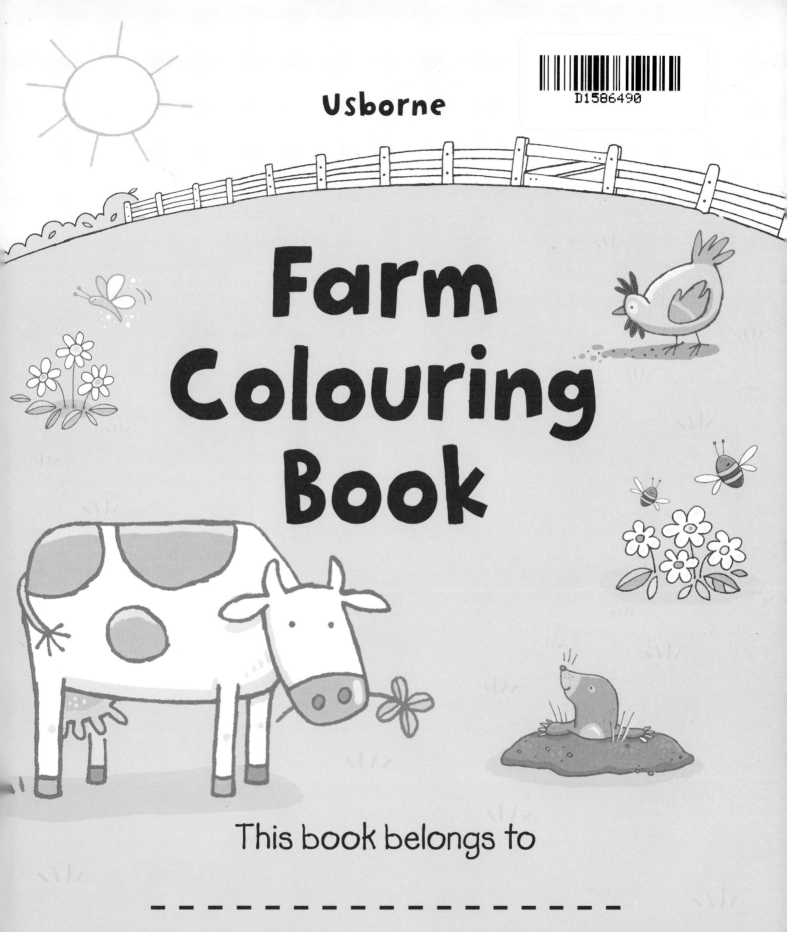

Usborne

Farm Colouring Book

This book belongs to

- - - - - - - - - - - - - - - - - - -

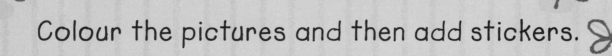

Colour the pictures and then add stickers.

Feeding the hens

Chicks

Henhouse

Hens

Eggs

Sun

Girl

Hens

Worm

In the farmyard

Trees

Barn

Tractor

Trailer

Bird

Gate

Butterflies

Flowers

In the fields

Cow

Calf

Sheepdog

Sheep

Bull

Mole

Lamb

Bird

Donkey

Cow

Rabbit

Goat

Horse

Foal

In the orchard

Tree

Apple

Dog

Beehive

Bee

In the vegetable garden

Cat

Gate

Wall

Wheelbarrow

Rabbits

Cabbages

Carrots

At the pond

Duckling

Ducks

Frog

Duck

Dragonfly

Fish

Lily pad

Goose

Snail

Flowers

Harvest time

Crows

Scarecrow

Tractor

Mouse

Night-time

Star

Moon

Owl

Cows

Tree

Fox

Barn

Cat

Tractor

Bat

Animal babies

Sheep

Cow

Lamb

Horse

Calf

Foal

Dog

Puppy

Chick

Hen